A Big

By Liza Charlesworth

ISBN: 978-1-339-02663-3

Art Director: Tannaz Fassihi; Designer: Tanya Chernyak
Photos © Getty Images.
Copyright © Liza Charlesworth. All rights reserved. Published by Scholastic Inc.

3 4 5 6 7 8 9 10   68   32 31 30 29 28 27 26 25 24

Printed in Jiaxing, China. First printing, August 2023.

M SCHOLASTIC

It is a big dog.
A dog can do a lot!

A dog can sit on top
of a rock.

A dog can hop.
It can hop on a log!

A dog and a mom
and a kid can jog.

If a dog is hot,
it can get wet.

A dog can pop in a box.

It can nap a lot.

A dog can be a pet.
It can get a big hug!